A WHOLE-STORY APPROACH **MID**

PAUL AND THE RACE FOR THE G

READING SKILLS IN CONTEXT

Written by Scott Angus Lauder

Published by Prim-Ed Publishing

Foreword

Enthusiasm for a 'good' read is not limited to adults. Younger readers are also appreciative of negotiating reading for a purpose other than merely demonstrating their ability.

Reading Skills in Context - Paul and the Race for the Gold Cup is a photocopiable story workbook to challenge younger pupils to read an adventure story and gain meaning and enthusiasm from their reading. It is suitable for pupils from the age of seven through to older children with special needs, who require help to develop their reading skills in the context of a high-interest short story. The story is organised into chapters, with each chapter having a unit of work consisting of:

- a chapter telling the next instalment of Paul's story;
- a cut and glue cartoon exercise, where the pupil creates their own book;
- a range of word study activities based on the chapter read; and
- suggestions for creative discussion, writing, research, art and design experiences.

Contents

Teachers Notes

Suggestions for Use

Reading Skills in Context - Paul and the Race for the Gold Cup, consists of 15 chapters, each organised into three-page work units:

Worksheet 1 starts with a chapter from the story *Paul and the Race for the Gold Cup*. This is ideal for a class shared reading activity or a group guided reading exercise. The teacher could extend the experience by discussing the use of vocabulary, grammar and punctuation in the story. As the story builds chapter by chapter, children could staple the pages to create their own book for individual reading.

The 'Be Creative' section provides an opportunity to extend the story using discussion, writing, research, art and design experiences. Suggestions for these activities are provided on page iii.

Worksheet 1

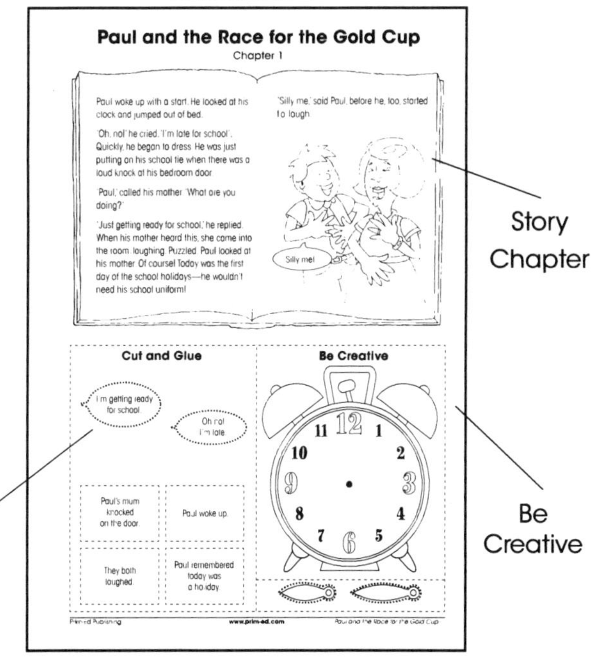

Paul and the Race for the Gold Cup

Chapter 1

Paul woke up with a start. He looked at his clock and jumped out of bed.

'Oh, no!' he cried. 'I'm late for school'. Quickly, he began to dress. He was just putting on his school tie when there was a loud knock at his bedroom door.

'Paul,' called his mother. 'What are you doing?'

'Just getting ready for school,' he replied. When his mother heard this, she came into the room laughing. Puzzled, Paul looked at his mother. Of course! Today was the first day of the school holidays—he wouldn't need his school uniform!

'Silly me,' said Paul, before he, too, started to laugh.

Story Chapter

Be Creative

Cut and Glue

Worksheet 2

Cartoon Comprehension

Worksheet 2 consists of a cartoon version of the chapter on the previous page. Pupils will need to re-read the chapter to remind themselves of the story. They will then need to cut out the speech bubbles and text boxes in the 'Cut and Glue' section on the previous page and glue them onto the correct place in the cartoon strip. As the cartoon builds chapter by chapter, children could staple the pages to create their own book for individual reading.

Worksheet 3

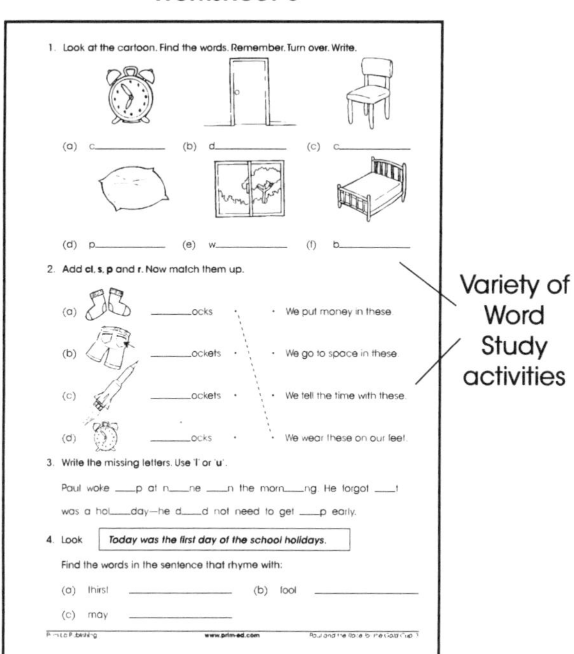

1. Look at the cartoon. Find the words. Remember. Turn over. Write.

(a) c______ (b) d______ (c) c______

(d) p______ (e) w______ (f) b______

2. Add cl, s, p and r. Now match them up.

(a) _____ocks • We put money in these.

(b) _____ockets • We go to space in these.

(c) _____ockets • We tell the time with these.

(d) _____ocks • We wear these on our feet.

3. Write the missing letters. Use 'i' or 'u'.

Paul woke __p at n__ne __n the morn__ng. He forgot __t was a hol__day—he d__d not need to get __p early.

4. Look. Today was the first day of the school holidays.

Find the words in the sentence that rhyme with:

(a) thirst ______ (b) fool ______

(c) may ______

Prim-Ed Publishing www.prim-ed.com Paul and the Race for the Gold Cup

Variety of Word Study activities

Worksheet 3 contains a variety of word study activities to develop knowledge of spelling and vocabulary. The word study activities are based on words used in the story chapter and cartoon on the previous two pages.

The word study activities include locating and spelling words form the text, initial sounds, definitions of words, rhyme, phonics, filling in missing letters from words and sorting sounds.

The story *Paul and the Race for the Gold Cup* may also provide the teacher with ideas for extending the work into both other areas of literacy and curriculum areas:

- drama (tableaux created through cartoons);
- vocabulary (word webs, personal dictionaries);
- research (sharks, transport, USA); and
- science (forces - friction, air resistance);
- geography (atlas work, map drawing, places);
- maths (time).

The story may also lend itself to a theme approach on 'Transport' (planes, taxis, boats, go-karts). However *Paul and the Race for the Gold Cup* is used we hope teachers and pupils will enjoy and benefit from it.

Be Creative

The following table provides suggested opportunities for the children to become more involved in discussion—helping to develop oral language skills. Many of the activities could also be extended to include writing, research, art and design experiences.

Chapter	Illustration	Text
1	Alarm clock with no hands	What time do you get up? Have you ever been late for school? Why were you late? Think of a good excuse. Who has the best excuse?
2	Cereal box, bowl and spoon	What is your favourite breakfast cereal? Make up a delicious new cereal. What ingredients will you include? What will you call it? Design a box for your cereal.
3	Aeroplane	Planes can fly. What other things fly? Have you ever been in a plane? Where did you go? If you had your own plane, where would you go? What would the inside of your plane look like?
4	Man running	Who is the fastest runner you know? Write a list of animals that can run faster than any man or woman.
5	Wanted poster with face missing	What do you think the kidnapper looks like? What reward would you give to catch the kidnapper? Make a 'Wanted' poster.
6	Shell and starfish	What other items might you find on a beach? Write a list of as many seashore items as possible.
7	Boat	If this boat was in a storm, what would the sea look like? What would happen if the boat began to sink? Draw the boat in a stormy sea.
8	Shark	Use nonfiction books to produce a fact file on sharks. Find the answers to the following: How do sharks breathe? What do sharks eat? How many types of sharks are there? Which oceans do sharks live in? Why can sharks be dangerous?
9	Jumping dolphin	Have you ever seen a dolphin? Why is the dolphin in the picture jumping? Draw a picture of a dolphin jumping for something.
10	Clothes	Do you wear a school uniform? What is it like? Design a new uniform for pupils and teachers to wear!
11	Words 'red' and 'green'	Look around the room. How many green and red things can you see? Write a list.
12	Sports/racing car	Were cars a hundred years ago the same as cars today? How have they changed? What do you think a car will look like one hundred years from now? Draw a picture and label the special parts.
13	Gold cup	Have you ever won anything? What prize would you give to someone who is a good swimmer, story writer or artist?
14	Racing driver clothes	A racing driver wears all of these clothes. What job would you like to do when you are older? Will you need to wear special clothes?

Curriculum Links - The National Literacy Strategy

The National Literacy Strategy focuses on a range of reading genres for each term. *Reading Skills in Context - Paul and the Race for the Gold Cup* is the ideal teaching tool for the adventure and mystery story and short novel reading range requirements for Years 3 and 4. It also suitable for use with older pupils with special educational needs.

The story and activities in *Reading Skills in Context - Paul and the Race for the Gold Cup* also covers the following word, sentence and text level requirements of the National Literacy Strategy:

Year	Term	Strand	
3	1,2,3	Word 2	• identify phonemes in writing, blend phonemes for reading and segment words into phonemes for spelling
3	1,2,3	Word 6	• use independent spelling strategies, including sounding out and spelling using phonemes, using visual skills, e.g. recognising common letter strings and spelling by analogy
3	1,2,3	Word 7	• practise new spellings by 'look, say, cover, write, check' strategy
3	1	Word 13	• collect new words from reading
3	2	Word 17	• continue the collection of new words from reading
3	3	Word 12	• continue the collection of new words from reading
3	1	Sentence 1	• use awareness of grammar to decipher new or unfamiliar words
3	1	Sentence 2	• take account of grammar and punctuation when reading aloud
3	1	Sentence 9	• notice and investigate a range of other devices for presenting text, e.g. speech bubbles, captions
3	1	Text 2	• know how dialogue is presented in stories
3	3	Text 1	• re-tell main points of a story in sequence
4	1,2,3	Word 1	• read and spell words through identifying phonemes in writing, blending phonemes for reading, segmenting words into phonemes for spelling, correct reading and spelling of high frequency words and using phonic/spelling knowledge as a cue, together with graphic, grammatical and contextual knowledge when reading unfamiliar texts
4	1,2,3	Word 3	• use independent spelling strategies, including sounding out and spelling using phonemes, using visual skills, e.g. recognising common letter strings and spelling by analogy
4	1,2,3	Word 4	• practise new spellings by 'look, say, cover, write, check' strategy
4	2	Word 6	• spell words with common endings: *-ight*, etc.
4	3	Word 5	• explore the occurrence of certain letter strings within words
4	3	Word 6	• spell words with common letter strings but different pronunciations
4	3	Text 3	• understand how paragraphs or chapters are used to collect, order and build up ideas

Paul and the Race for the Gold Cup

Chapter 1

Paul woke up with a start. He looked at his clock and jumped out of bed.

'Oh, no!' he cried. 'I'm late for school'. Quickly, he began to dress. He was just putting on his school tie when there was a loud knock at his bedroom door.

'Paul,' called his mother. 'What are you doing?'

'Just getting ready for school,' he replied. When his mother heard this, she came into the room, laughing. Puzzled, Paul looked at his mother. Of course! Today was the first day of the school holidays—he wouldn't need his school uniform!

'Silly me,' said Paul, before he, too, started to laugh.

Cut and Glue

I'm getting ready for school.

Oh no! I'm late.

Paul's mum knocked on the door.	Paul woke up.
They both laughed.	Paul remembered today was a holiday.

Be Creative

clock
pillow
bed

What are you doing?
knock knock
window
door
chair

HOLIDAY!

Silly me!

1. **Look at the cartoon. Find the words. Remember. Turn over. Write.**

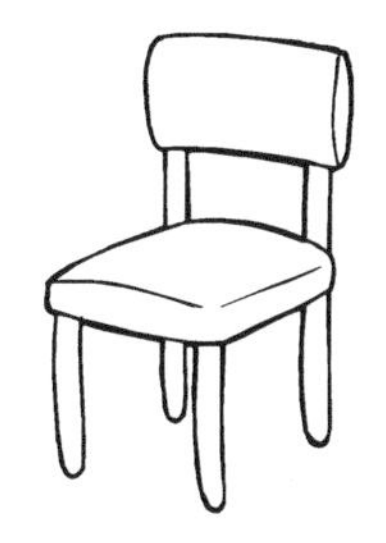

(a) c__________ (b) d__________ (c) c__________

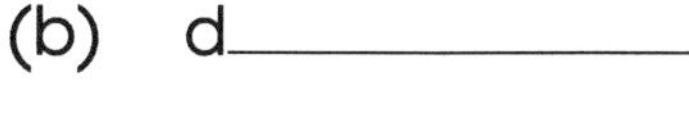

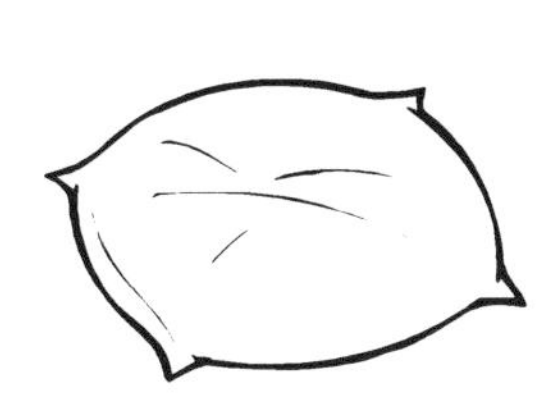
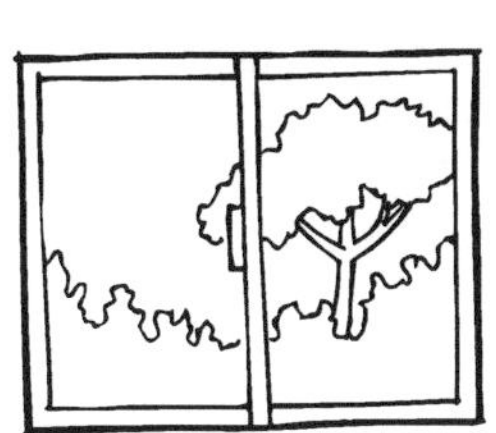

(d) p__________ (e) w__________ (f) b__________

2. **Add cl, s, p and r. Now match them up.**

(a)  ______ocks • • We put money in these.

(b)  ______ockets • • We go to space in this.

(c) 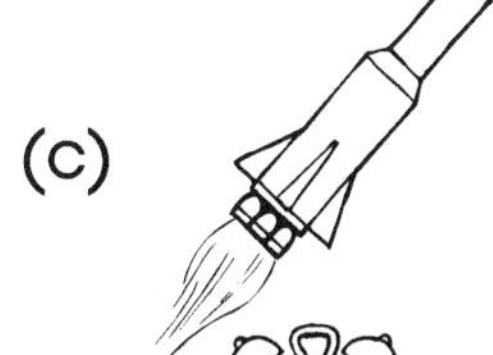 ______ocket • • We tell the time with this.

(d)  ______ock • • We wear these on our feet.

3. **Write the missing letters. Use 'i' or 'u'.**

Paul woke ___p at n___ne ___n the morn___ng. He forgot ___t was a hol___day. He d___d not need to get ___p early.

4. **Look**

Today was the first day of the school holidays.

Find the words in the sentence that rhyme with:

(a) thirst __________ (b) fool __________

(c) may __________

Paul and the Race for the Gold Cup

Chapter 2

Paul came down the stairs and sat at the kitchen table.

'What's for breakfast, Mum?' he asked. 'I'm starving.' His mother smiled.

'Try this,' she said, handing him a big box of cereal.

'"Tasties",' he said, reading the name from the box. 'I haven't tried these before.'

'I know,' Mum said. 'I couldn't get your favourite.'

'Oh well, never mind,' Paul shrugged, as he poured cereal into his bowl. Suddenly, a small yellow card fell out of the box.

Paul picked it up and read it.

Paul was amazed.

Cut and Glue

Try this.

I've won!

Paul read the yellow card.	Paul read the name on the box.
Paul came downstairs.	Paul asked what was for breakfast.

Be Creative

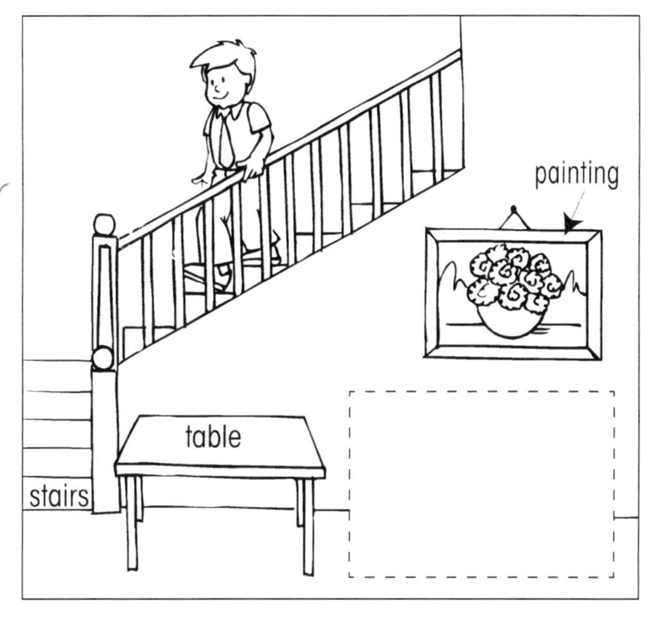
painting
table
stairs

What's for breakfast, Mum?

Tasties
Win a trip to the Go-Kart Gold Cup
box

'TASTIES'. I've never tasted these before.
Tasties
bowl

card
Tasties

1. **Look at the cartoon. Find the words. Remember. Turn over. Write.**

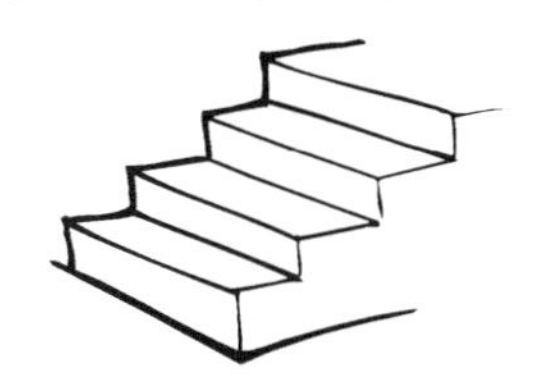

(a) s__________ (b) b__________ (c) t__________

(d) p__________ (e) b__________ (f) c__________

2. **Sort the sounds.**

	sounds like 'c**a**me'	sounds like 'c**ar**'
*h**ar**d* *k**ar**t*	__________	__________
*p**ai**nt* *t**a**ste*	__________	__________
*n**a**me* *s**a**me*	__________	__________
*m**ar**k*	__________	

3. **Write the missing letters. Use 'a' or 'o'.**

P___ul re___d the c___rd. It s___id he h___d w___n ___ trip t___ Americ___ ___nd the ch___nce t___ r___ce in the G___-K___rt G___ld Cup. P___ul w___s delighted.

4. **Fill in. Use 'st' or 'sl'.**

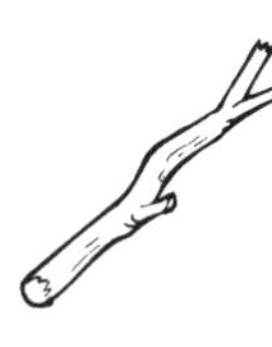

(a) ______rong (b) ______ow (c) ______ick

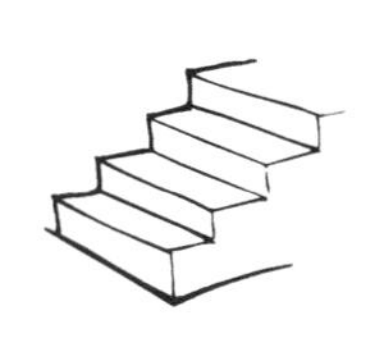

(d) ______airs (e) ______eep (f) ______ip

Paul and the Race for the Gold Cup

Chapter 3

Paul asked his mother if he could go.

'Can I go, Mum? Please?'

He asked again and again. At first, his mother said no. But she finally gave in and said yes.

Within no time, Paul was flying to America. When he arrived, a woman from 'Tasties' met him and took him to his hotel in a big black car. Paul felt like a film star!

'This is where you'll be staying,' the woman said. Paul looked at the hotel. It was huge.

'Tomorrow is the practice day, and the day after that is the real race,' said the woman.

'See you tomorrow.'

'OK,' said Paul. He waved goodbye.

Nobody saw the strange man who was watching them carefully.

Cut and Glue

Mum, can I go? Please!

Hello, my name is Paul.

This is your hotel.

Paul asked if he could go.	Someone was watching them.
The woman took Paul to his hotel.	The woman, from 'Tasties' met him at the airport.

Be Creative

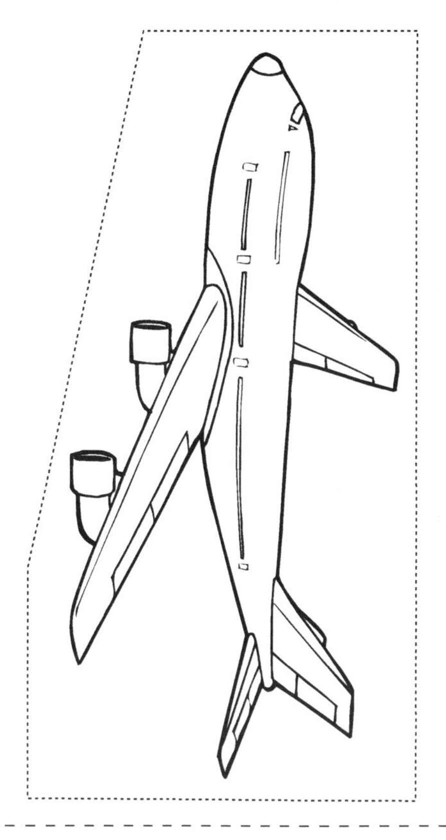

Yes, I suppose so.

America here I come!
seat

plane
Nice to meet you.
road
wheel

hotel

tree

1. Look at the cartoon. Find the words. Remember. Turn over. Write.

(a) t________ (b) s________ (c) h________

(d) p________ (e) r________ (f) w________

2. Use '**oa**' or '**ee**'. Now match up.

(a) t____d • • This is black and we burn it.

(b) c____l • • Something cars drive along.

(c) sp____d • • This is like a big frog.

(d) str____t • • This means to travel fast.

3. Write the missing letters. Use '**e**' or '**i**'.

Paul w___nt to Am___r___ca ___n a plan___. Th___r___ w___r___ mor___ than two hundr___d p___opl___ ___n ___t. Th___ plan___ was a jumbo j___t.

4. Look **_Nobody saw the strange man who was watching them._**

Find the words in the sentence that rhyme with:

(a) can, fan, ran ________ (b) two, you, knew ________

(c) range ________ (d) paw ________

Paul and the Race for the Gold Cup

Chapter 4

That night, Paul ate dinner in his hotel and then went to bed.

Early the next morning, he took a taxi to the racetrack. When he got there, he was given go-kart number 9—his favourite number.

On the track, some racers were already practising hard. The fastest so far was go-kart number 4. His time was two minutes and 14 seconds.

'I think I can beat that!' Paul said confidently. He got into his kart and zoomed around the track. He looked at his time. It was two minutes and 10 seconds.

'Yes!' shouted Paul. 'I'm four seconds faster than anyone else!' Feeling happy, he left the track and walked back to his hotel. He could hardly wait for the real race.

Cut and Glue

I think I can win the real race tomorrow.

Yes! I'm the fastest.

Lots of people watched the racers.	Paul beat the fastest time.
Paul walked back to the hotel.	Paul took a taxi to the stadium.

Be Creative

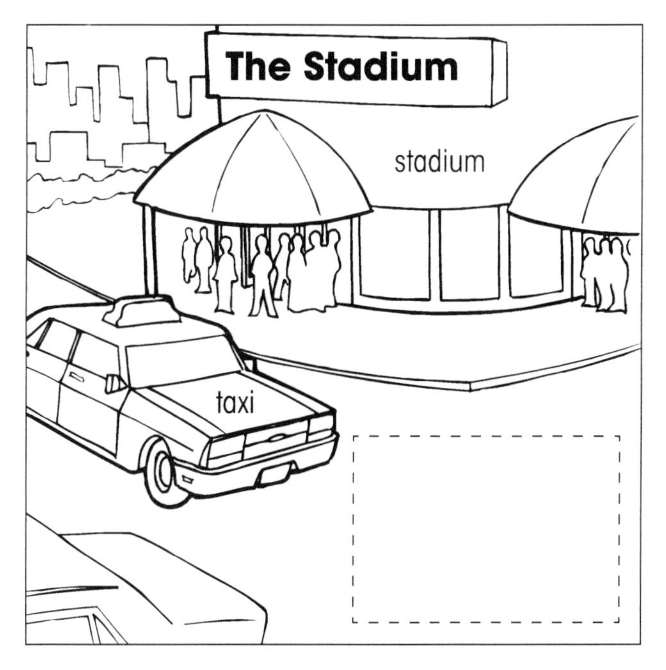
The Stadium
stadium
taxi

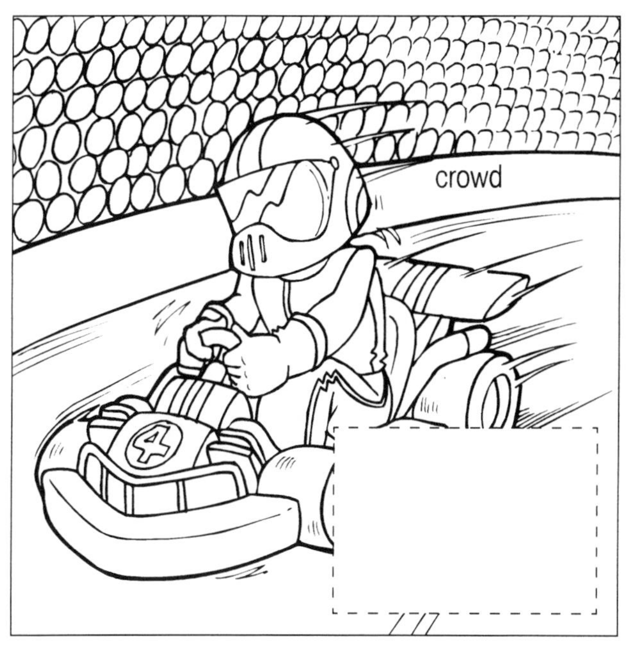
crowd

helmet
gloves
2 MIN. 10 SEC.
grass
FINISH

1. **Look at the cartoon. Find the words. Remember. Turn over. Write.**

(a) g__________ (b) g__________ (c) h__________

(d) c__________ (e) t__________ (f) s__________

2. **Sort the sounds.**

	sounds like 't**a**lk'	sounds like 't**a**xi'
*s**a**w* *w**a**lk*	__________	__________
*c**a**n* *f**a**n*	__________	__________
*pl**a**n* *t**a**ll*	__________	__________
*ch**a**lk*	__________	

3. **Write the missing letters. Use 'i' or 'e'.**

Paul's t___m___ of two m___nut___s and t___n s___conds was th___ fast___st. No-on___ ___ls___ could b___at it. Paul was sur___ h___ could w___n the r___al rac___ tomorrow.

4. **Fill in. Use 'cr' or 'tr'.**

(a) ______eam (b) ______umpet (c) s______eam

(d) ______owd (e) s______ipes (f) s______ing

Paul and the Race for the Gold Cup

Chapter 5

That evening, Paul again had dinner in his hotel, before going to his room and watching television. Soon he was feeling very tired. He looked at his watch. It was 10 o'clock. Paul got into bed and switched off the light. Before long, he was fast asleep.

Suddenly, Paul woke up. He looked around the room. It was very dark. Was he imagining things, or had he heard a noise? Slowly, he reached out for the lamp beside his bed. Out of the darkness, a cold hand grabbed his. Paul screamed as a hood was thrown over his head. He tried to fight, but his arms and legs were tied tightly. He heard the bedroom window slide open, then felt himself being lifted off the bed. He could not believe what happened next. Somebody threw him out of the window!

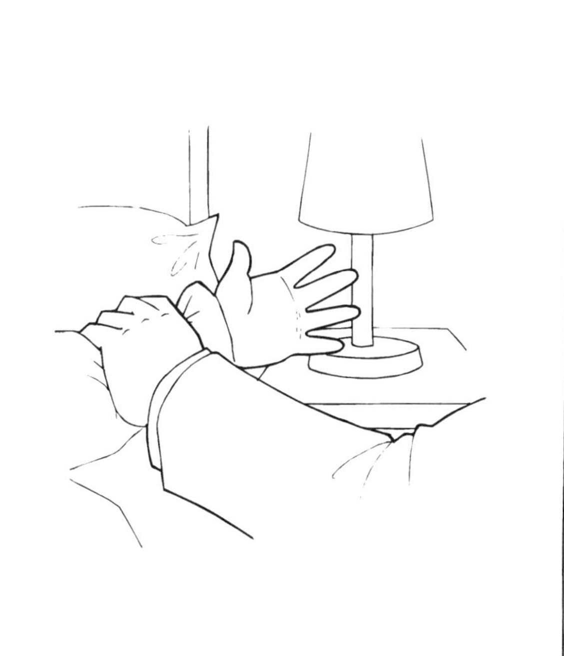

Cut and Glue

What was that noise?

Delicious!

Someone grabbed Paul.

Paul fell asleep.

Paul had dinner at the hotel.

They threw him out of the window.

Suddenly Paul woke up.

Be Creative

WANTED

for ______________________

reward ______________________

hamburger
glass

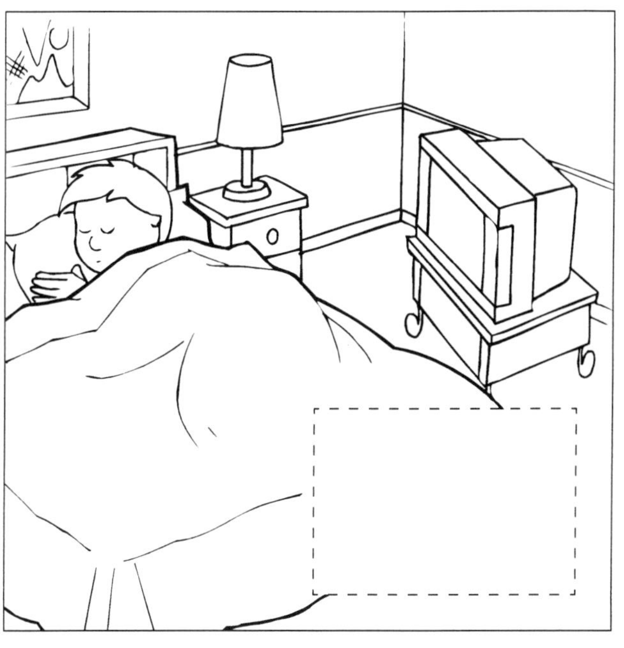

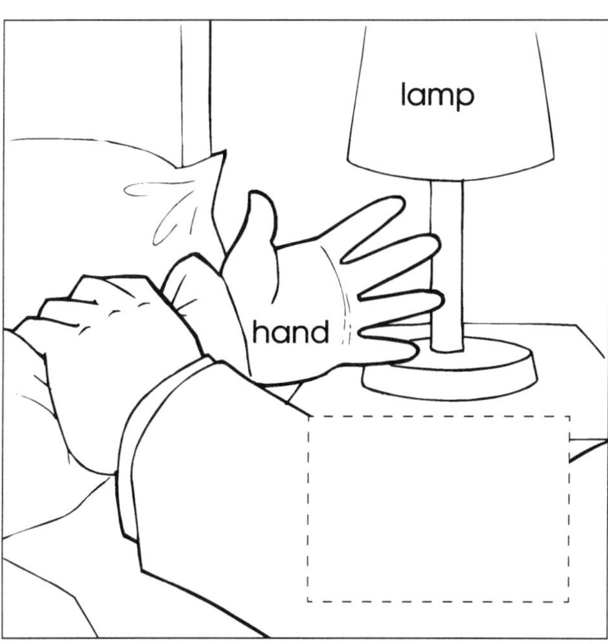
lamp
hand

hood
rope

1. **Look at the cartoon. Find the words. Remember. Turn over. Write.**

(a) h__________ (b) h__________ (c) r__________

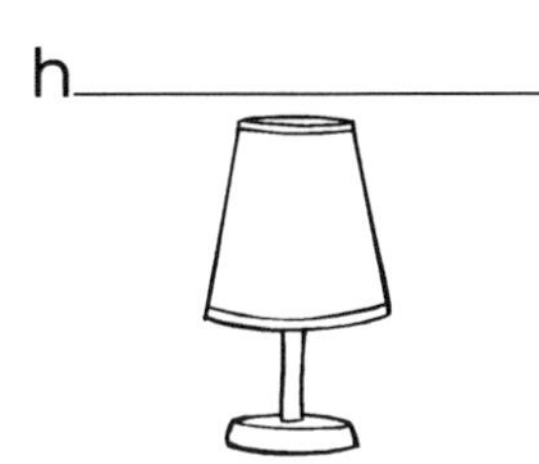
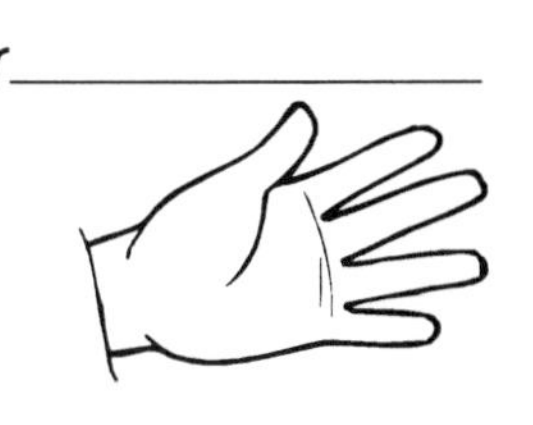

(d) g__________ (e) l__________ (f) h__________

2. **Use 'gl' or 'sw'. Now match up.**

(a)  ________ass • • It is either off or on.

(b)  ________ing • • It is easy to break.

(c) 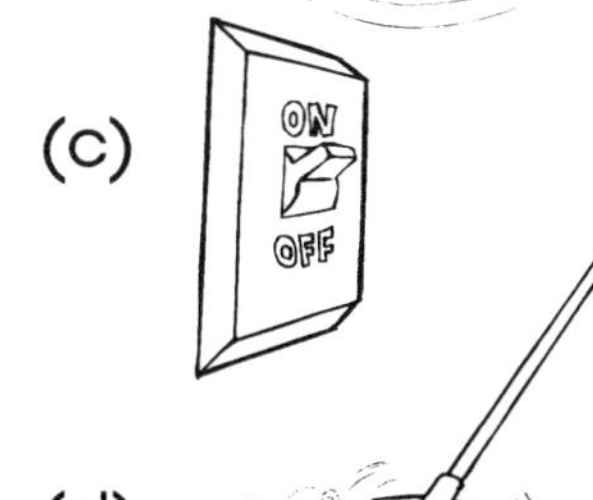

________itch • • It is what we do when we use a broom.

(d) ________eep • • It is something we play on.

3. **Write the missing letters. Use 'a' or 'u'.**

S____ddenly P____ul felt ____ h____nd on his. He j____mped ____p b____t the men were too strong. They tied him ____p ____nd threw him he____d first o____t of the window.

4. **Look** ***Paul got into bed and before long he was fast asleep.***

Find the words in the sentence that rhyme with:

(a) red, head, said __________ (b) last, cast, mast __________

(c) what, rot, knot __________ (d) see, we, knee __________

Paul and the Race for the Gold Cup

Chapter 6

'Help!' Paul screamed as he tumbled through the air. But instead of hitting the hard ground below, he landed with a crash in the back of truck full of empty cardboard boxes.

'Ouch!' he shouted. But before he could move, the truck zoomed off.

'Where are you taking me?' he yelled. But no-one answered. The truck roared through the night with Paul in the back. After a long while, it stopped. Paul could not see a thing, but he could hear waves crashing, and the air smelt salty.

Paul was really puzzled. Why was he near the beach? Who had kidnapped him? And why? He had no idea. Nearby, a boat started its engines and Paul heard footsteps coming towards him.

Cut and Glue

Where are you taking me?

Ouch!

The truck zoomed off.

Paul landed in the truck with a crash.

Paul shouted to the driver but no-one answered.

In the distance Paul heard a boat start its engines.

Be Creative

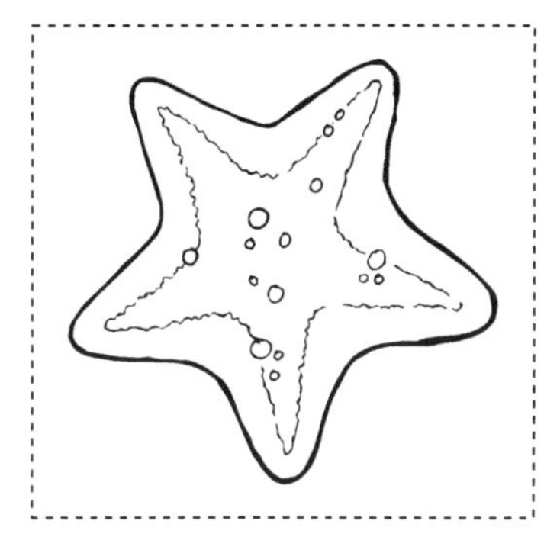

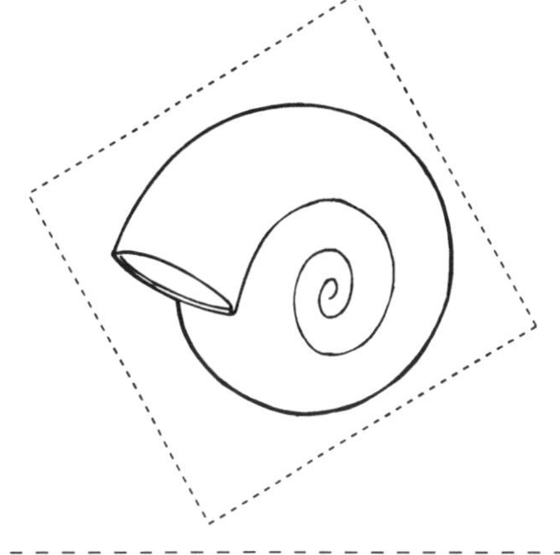

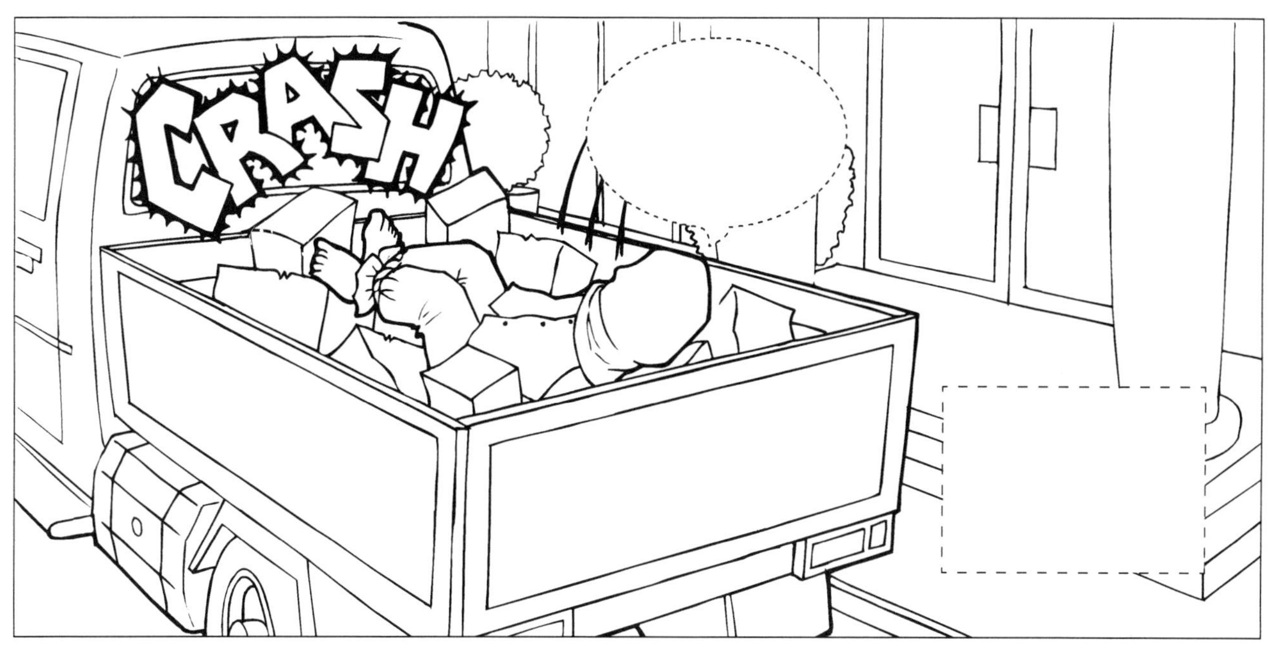
CRASH

ZOOM
truck
headlights

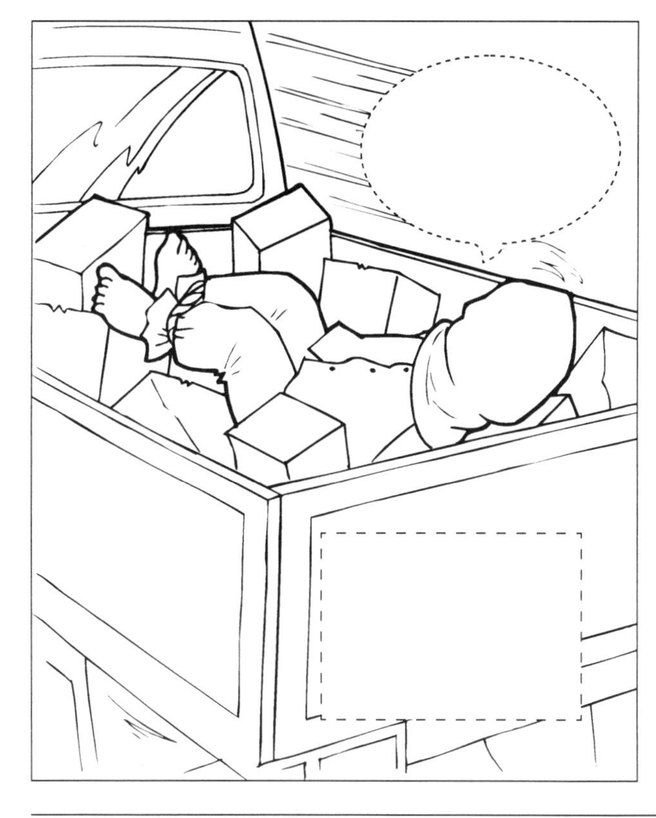

moon
boat
BROOM
jetty
starfish

1. **Look at the cartoon. Find the words. Remember. Turn over. Write.**

(a) m________ (b) s________ (c) b________

(d) t________ (e) j________ (f) h________

2. **Sort the sounds.**

*sn**o**w*	*t**u**be*
*bel**o**w*	*cr**o**w*
*r**oo**f*	*r**u**de*
*sp**oo**n*	*g**oa**t*

sounds like 'b**oa**t'	sounds like 'm**oo**n'
________	________
________	________
________	________
________	________

3. **Write the missing letters. Use 'a', 'e' or 'o'.**

___ft___r ___ whil___ th___ truck st___pp___d. P___ul c___uld

n___t s___ ___ ___nything but h___ n___tic___d th___t th___

___ir sm___lt s___lty ___nd th___r___ w___s th___ n___is___

___f w___v___s in th___ dist___nc___.

4. **Add 'l', 'f', 'he' or 'n'. Now match them up.**

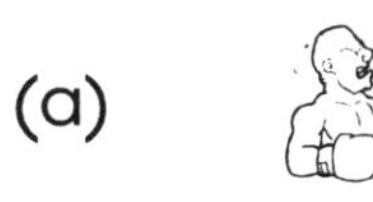

(a)  ___ight • • This is how tall you are.

(b)  ___ight • • This is what boxers do.

(c)  ___ight • • This is when we can see stars.

(d)  ___ight • • This is bright.

Paul and the Race for the Gold Cup

Chapter 7

Paul felt himself picked up and carried. The noise of the boat's engines got louder and louder.

'Where are you taking me?' Paul shouted. Instead of answering, the people carrying him dropped Paul on the deck of the boat. He landed with a heavy thud.

'Don't move,' said a deep voice. Paul was scared. When the kidnapper spoke, there was a strange clicking noise, like coins jingling in a pocket.

'What a strange noise,' thought Paul. But he said nothing.

He lay quietly while the boat started to move. Soon, it was far from land. Paul was now really afraid. What were the kidnappers going to do with him?

Suddenly, his arms and legs were grabbed. He screamed, but his kidnappers just laughed. Before he could say another word, they threw him headfirst into the sea!

Cut and Glue

HELP!

Don't move!

Paul was thrown into the sea.

Paul lay quietly as the boat headed out to sea.

Paul was thrown onto the deck.

Be Creative

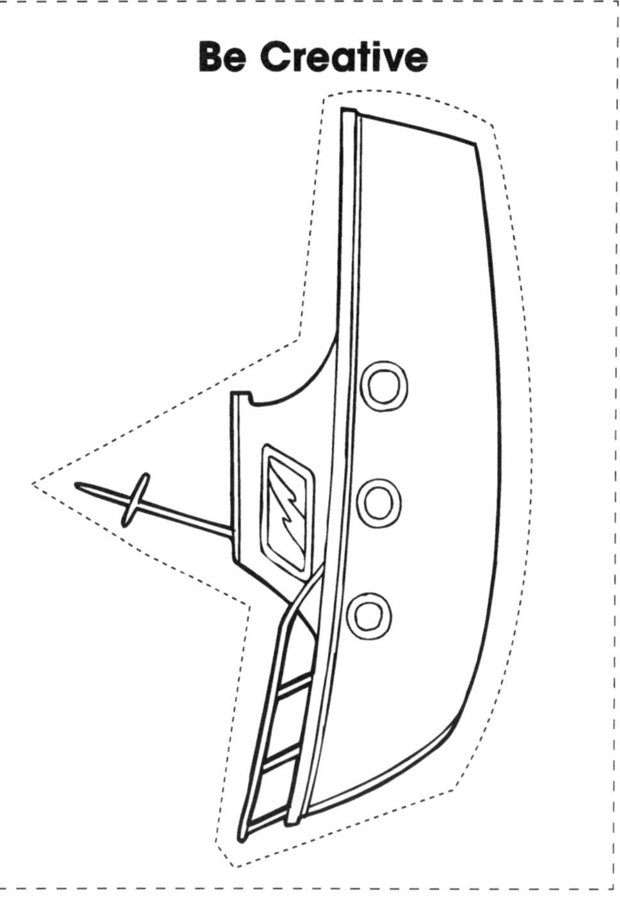

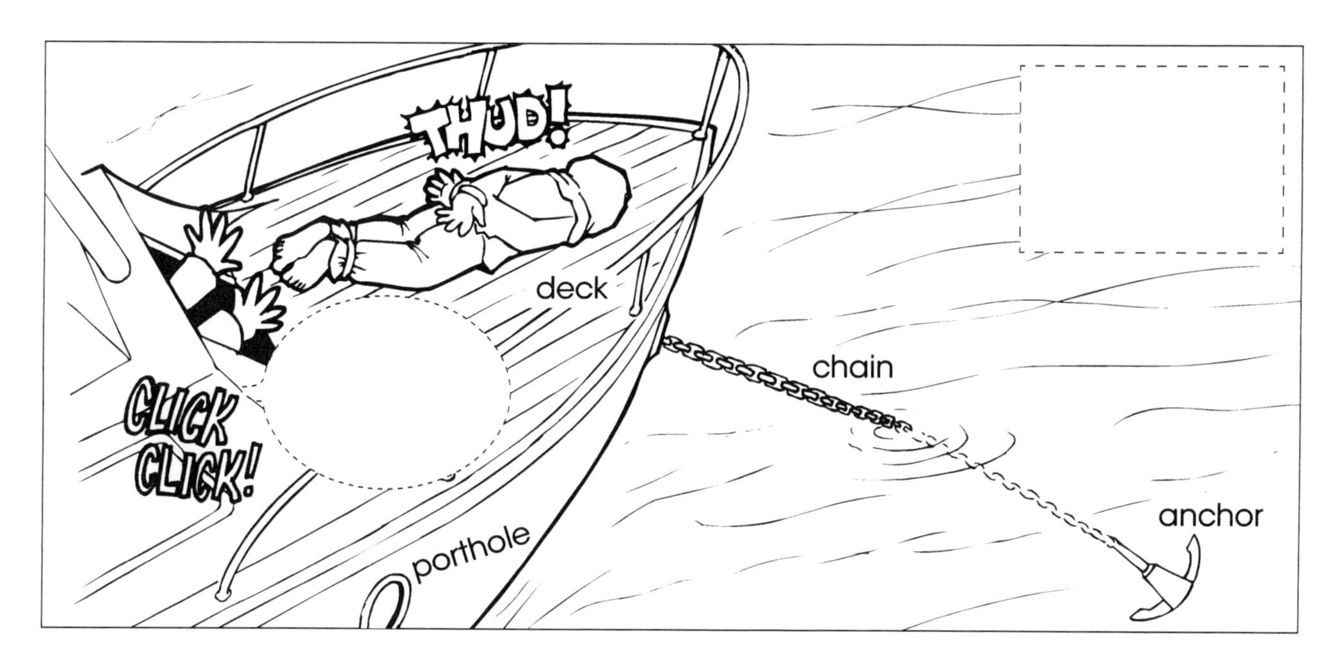
THUD!
deck
chain
CLICK CLICK!
porthole
anchor

cabin
bow

HA HAHAHA-HA!

1. **Look at the cartoon. Find the words. Remember. Turn over. Write.**

(a) c____________ (b) a____________ (c) d____________

(d) p____________ (e) b____________ (f) c____________

2. **Use 'ick' or 'eck'. Now match them up.**

(a) tr____________ • • Not a ship to sail in.

(b) n____________ • • Not your shoulders.

(c) qu____________ • • Not real. It's magic.

(d) shipwr____________ • • Not slow.

3. **Write the missing letters. Use 'u', 'o' or 'a'.**

S___ddenly P___ ___l w___s picked ___p ___nd thr___wn int___ the se___. He l___nded in the w___ter with ___ h___ge spl___sh. The kidn___ppers j___st l___ ___ghed.

4. **Look** ***Paul landed on the deck of the boat with a thud!***

Find the words in the sentence that rhyme with:

(a) call, small, wall ____________

(b) float, note, wrote ____________

(c) blood, mud, flood ____________

(d) neck, wreck, peck ____________

Paul and the Race for the Gold Cup

Chapter 8

The hood came off in the water and Paul looked around. He could hardly believe his eyes. The boat was sailing away without him!

'Hey! Come back!' he shouted. But it just kept going until he could not see it any more.

He struggled with his ropes until he was able to untie his feet and hands.

'Now what am I going to do?' he asked himself gloomily. He looked at the city lights shining in the distance. 'It's too far to swim.'

A sudden noise behind him made Paul spin round in the water. He gasped with horror. There, shining in the moonlight, was a shark's fin—rushing straight towards him!

Cut and Glue

It's too far to swim.

Come back!

What's that noise?

Paul saw a shark's fin rushing towards him.

Paul heard a noise behind him.

The boat sailed away.

The city lights were very far away.

Be Creative

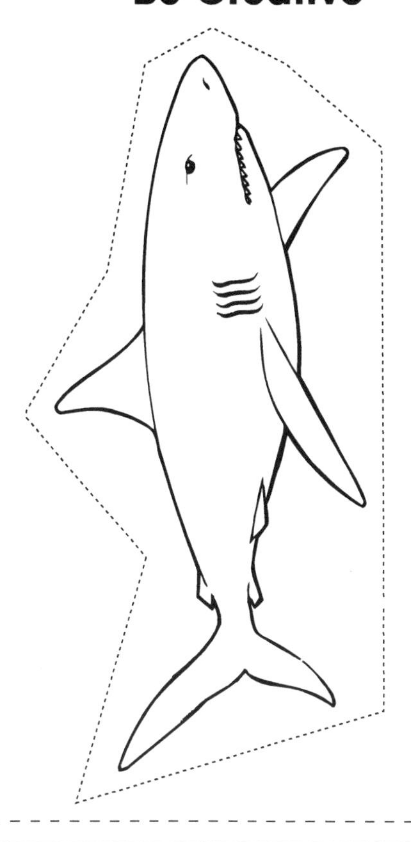

mast
angry

coast
sad

surprised

fin
oh no!

1. Look at the cartoon. Find the words. Remember. Turn over. Write.

(a) s__________ (b) f__________ (c) m__________

(d) c__________ (e) a__________ (f) s__________

2. Sort the sounds.

	sounds like 'f**i**nd'	sounds like 'f**i**n'
*t**i**e* *sh**i**ne*	______	______
*g**i**nger* *l**i**ght*	______	______
*w**i**nner* *f**i**ght*	______	______
*sw**i**mmer* *h**i**m*	______	______

3. Write the missing letters. Use '**i**', '**o**' or '**a**'.

When the b___ ___t s___ ___led ___w___y P___ul felt very

___fr___ ___d. The c___ ___st w___s t___ ___ f___r t___

sw___m t___. P___ ___l w___s ___l___ne ___n the m___ddle

___f the se___ w___th n___-___ne t___ help h___m.

4. Add '**ark**' or '**urn**'.

(a) b__________ing (b) t__________ (c) m__________er pen

(d) sh__________ (e) f__________iture (f) b__________

Paul and the Race for the Gold Cup

Chapter 9

The shark opened its jaws and Paul saw its teeth gleaming. Just when he was sure he would be eaten, something very strange happened. Without warning, the shark spun around and quickly swam away. Paul was amazed. What had happened? Why hadn't the shark eaten him? Paul was puzzled—until three dolphins leapt out of the sea and splashed down beside him.

'So it was you!' Paul yelled as he gratefully grabbed one of the dolphins' fins. Paul knew they had saved his life by rushing at the shark and frightening it away.

'Let's go!' he shouted, and the dolphin began to pull him towards dry land.

Cut and Glue

Let's go!

Oh no!

The dolphins began to pull Paul towards land.	The shark opened its mouth wide.
Three dolphins leapt into the air.	The shark turned away.

Be Creative

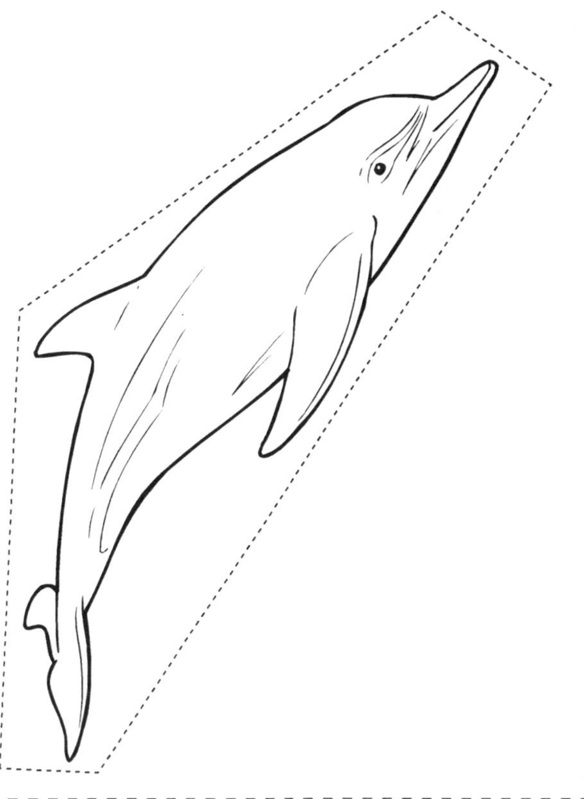

nose
eye
teeth
mouth

dolphin
happy

1. **Look at the cartoon. Find the words. Remember. Turn over. Write.**

(a) h__________ (b) m__________ (c) e__________

(d) t__________ (e) n__________ (f) d__________

2. **Add 'b', 'c', 'h', 'n', 'p' or 'r'. Then match the word.**

(a) ____ase (b) ____ose

(c) ____ase (d) ____ose

(e) ____ose (f) ____aste

long	(b)	heavy	____
sticky	____	red	____
runny	____	secret	____

3. **Write the missing letters. Use 'i', 'o' or 'u'.**

When Pa____l saw the shark's h____ge teeth gleam____ng ____n the m____ ____nl____ght he felt very afra____d. He was s____re the shark was ab____ ____t t____ eat h____m f____r d____nner.

4. **Look**

> ***'Let's go!' shouted Paul and the three dolphins began to pull him towards dry land.***

Find the words in the sentence that rhyme with:

(a) cry, fry, try ____________

(b) free, knee, sea ____________ ____________

(c) bull, full ____________

(d) hand, sand, band ____________

Paul and the Race for the Gold Cup

Chapter 10

It was morning before Paul reached the shore. He waved goodbye to the dolphins and began the long walk to the stadium. He was still dressed in his pyjamas.

Paul reached the stadium just in time for his race. He ran inside and went straight to his go-kart. Paul was just about to pull on his helmet when he heard the strange clicking sound from the night before. He turned around. Beside go-kart number 4 was a man dressed in a white suit. Paul looked at the man, who smiled back. Paul stared in horror. The man had gold teeth—that was the clicking sound Paul had heard on the boat. This man was one of his kidnappers!

Cut and Glue

Paul stared at the man in the white suit.	Paul ran to his go-kart.
Paul said goodbye to the dolphins.	Paul heard the strange clicking noise again.
The man smiled and Paul realised he was one of the kidnappers.	Paul saw the stadium ahead.

Be Creative

GOODBYE

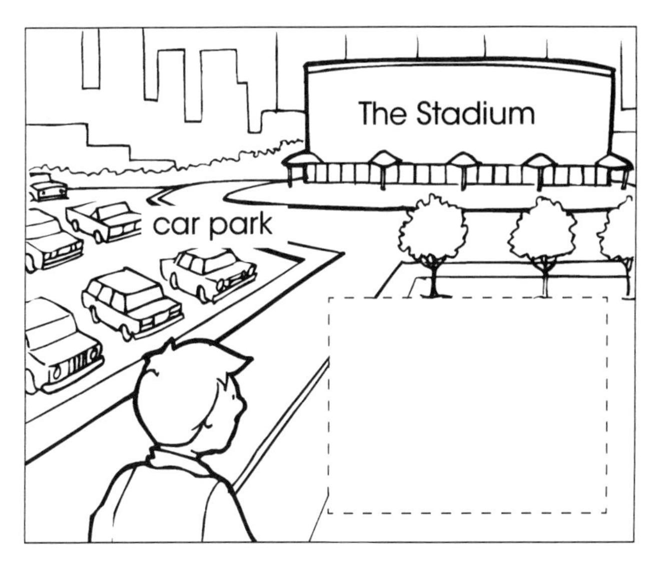
The Stadium
car park

nine

CLICK
CLICK!

four
suit

white hat
gold teeth
HA
HA
HA!

1. **Look at the cartoon. Find the words. Remember. Turn over. Write.**

(a) c_____ p_____ (b) s_________ (c) g_____ t_____

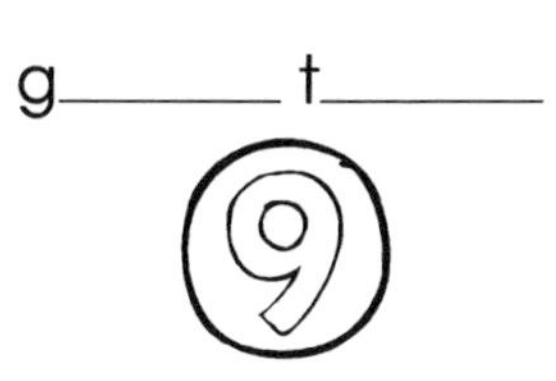

(d) w_____ h_____ (e) f_________ (f) n___________

2. **Sort the sounds.**

	sounds like 't**ee**th'	sounds like 't**e**n'
*p**ea**nut* *pl**ea**se*	______________	______________
*n**e**xt* *sl**ee**p*	______________	______________
*l**e**ft* *sp**ea**k*	______________	______________
*t**e**nt* *w**e***	______________	______________
*pl**e**nty* *r**ea**dy*	______________	______________

3. **Write the missing letters. Use '*a*', '*e*' or '*i*'.**

P____ul r____n ____ns____d____ th____ st____d____um ____nd w____nt str____ ____ght to h____s go-k____rt. Luck____ly th____ r____c____ h____d not st____rt____d y____t. H____ w____s just ____bout to put on h____s h____lm____t wh____n h____ h____ ____rd ____ str____ng____ no____s____.

4. **Add '*old*' or '*oll*'.**

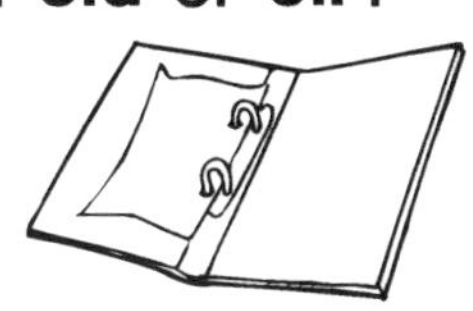

(a) f_________er (b) l_________y (c) s_________ier

(d) c_________ (e) r_________ercoaster (f) d_________

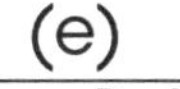

Paul and the Race for the Gold Cup

Chapter 11

'I need to find a police officer,' thought Paul. But his race was about to start. After all he had been through, he did not want to miss his chance of winning the gold cup. Quickly, he pulled on his helmet and drove to the start line. He saw the boy in kart number 4 stare at him. Suddenly, Paul remembered there had been *two* people in his hotel room and on the boat. But why had the boy in kart 4 helped the man with the gold teeth? Paul wanted to speak to the other boy, but before he could say anything the starting lights flashed from red to green.

'Go!' thought Paul, and he zoomed away as fast as he could. The race had started—and he was in the lead!

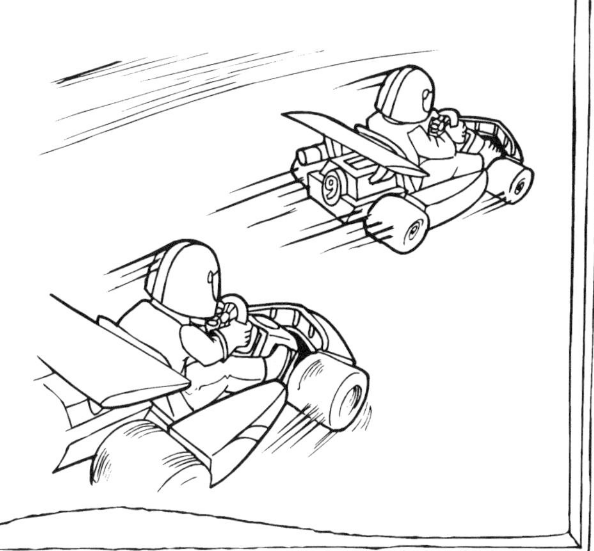

Cut and Glue

I don't have time to find a police officer.

Why did you help the man with gold teeth?

Paul zoomed into the lead.

The lights turned to green.

The bell rang to tell drivers to go to the start line.

Paul drove to the start line.

Paul stared at the boy in go-kart number 4.

Be Creative

BRINNNG!
bell

START

red
twelve
tyres

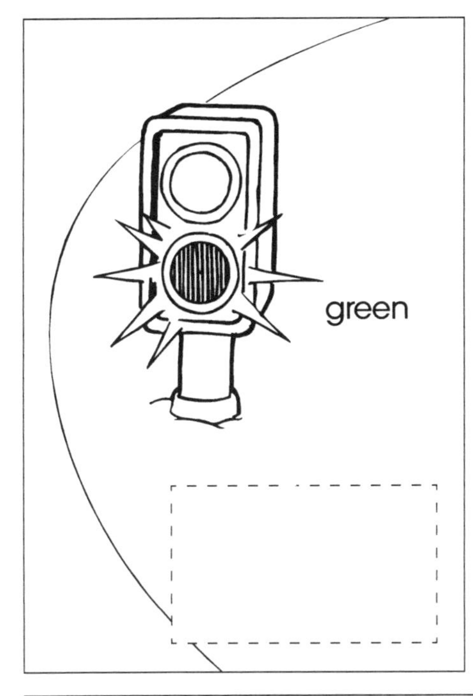
green

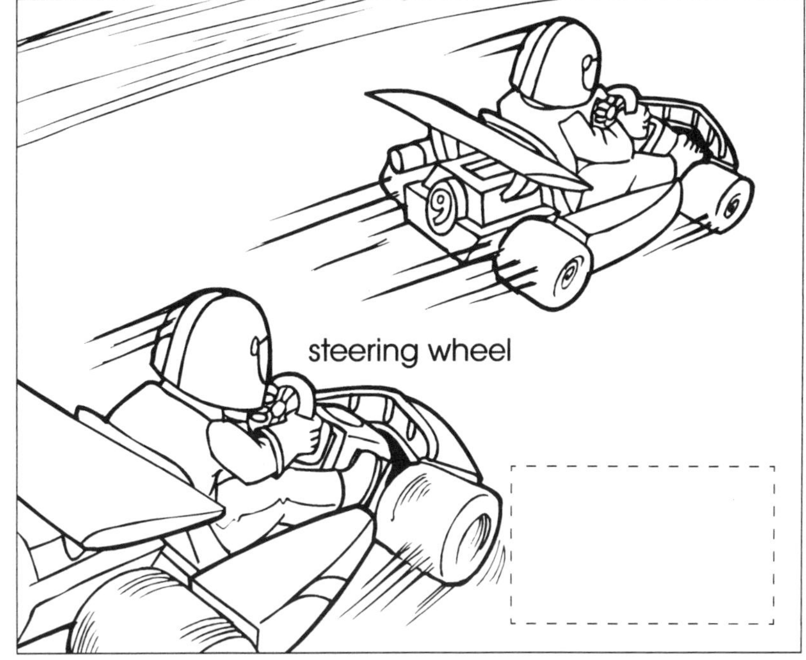
steering wheel

1. Look at the cartoon. Find the words. Remember. Turn over. Write.

(a) r________ (b) s__________ w__________ (c) g__________

(d) b________ (e) t__________ (f) t__________

2. Add '**irt**' or '**ire**'. Then match the word.

(a) sh________ (b) th________y

(c) f________ (d) f________work

(e) w________ (f) b________hday

happy	(f)	warm	____
sharp	____	clean	____
number	____	loud	____

3. Write the missing letters. Use '**e**', '**o**' or '**u**'.

Pa___l was sitting at the start lin___ wh___n h___

r___m___mb___r___d that th___r___ had b___ ___n tw___

p___ ___pl___ in his h___t___l r___ ___m and in th___

b___at.

4. Look

The lights changed from red to green and the race began.

Find the words in the sentence that rhyme with:

(a) face, place, lace ____________________

(b) tonight, fight, might ____________________

(c) bread, said, bed ____________________

(d) queen, been, bean ____________________

Paul and the Race for the Gold Cup

Chapter 12

Round and round the track the karts raced. Louder and louder the crowd cheered. It was the last corner on the last lap. Paul was still in the lead, but number 4 was close behind. Neck-and-neck the two boys raced towards the finish line. Suddenly, number 4 tried to overtake, but he lost control and hit the kerb. Paul watched in horror as the kart skidded into the wall and crashed. The crowd went silent. The boy was trapped beneath his go-kart. If Paul kept going, he would win the gold cup—but that would mean not helping the other boy.

Paul braked hard and ran to the crashed kart.

'Don't worry!' Paul yelled, and he pulled the boy away. Go-kart number 4 exploded—but both boys were safe.

Cut and Glue

Thanks! You saved my life.

Come on number 4!

The boys raced faster and faster.

Paul stopped and pulled the boy out.

Number 4 crashed.

Number 4 exploded.

The crowd cheered and cheered.

Be Creative

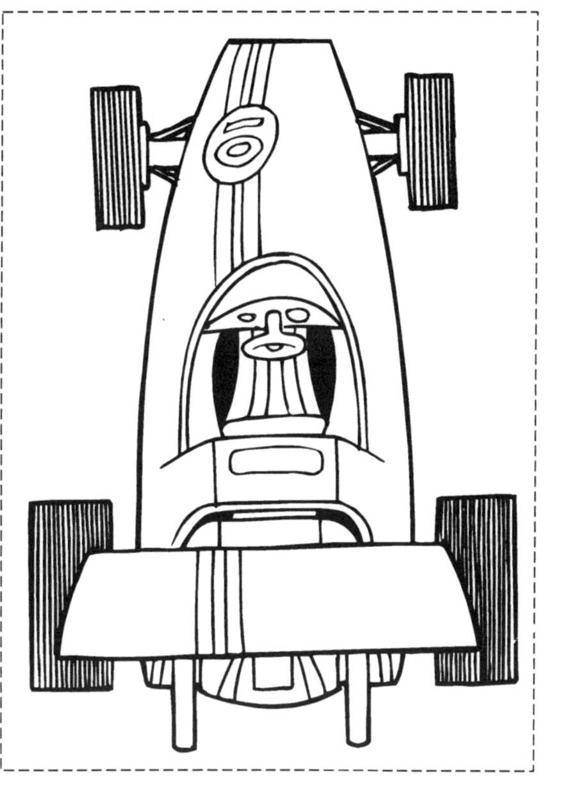

shout
watch

race

crash

pull

explode

1. **Look at the cartoon. Find the words. Remember. Turn over. Write.**

(a) c______ (b) p______ (c) s______

(d) e______ (e) w______ (f) r______

2. **Sort the sounds.**

	sounds like 'sh**ou**t'	sounds like 'sh**u**t'
*sh**o**wer* *m**u**st*	______	______
*j**u**mp* *p**o**wer*	______	______
*c**o**me* *m**ou**se*	______	______
*t**o**wer* *br**u**sh*	______	______
*h**ou**r* ***u**pstairs*	______	______

3. **Add the missing letters. Use 'a', 'o' or 'u'.**

____fter the b____y in n____mber 4 cr____shed, the cr____wd went silent. P____ ____l decided t____ st____p. If P____ ____l h____d n____t st____pped, he w____ ____ld h____ve w____n the race. Bec____ ____se P____ ____l did st____p the b____y w____s n____t b____dly h____rt.

4. **Add 'ash' or 'ish'.**

(a) goldf______ (b) sm______ (c) w______

(d) r______ (e) cr______ (f) d______

Paul and the Race for the Gold Cup

Chapter 13

Paul heard a roar from the crowd and looked up. There at the finish line was the man with the gold teeth. He had just snatched the gold cup off the table—he was trying to steal it! Paul jumped into his go-kart and drove straight at the man.

'Thump!' went the man as the go-kart hit him. As soon as he landed on the ground, the police grabbed him and put him in handcuffs.

The man shouted angrily, but the police were delighted. 'Well done,' they said to Paul. But Paul was still puzzled. He did not understand why the boy had helped the man with the gold teeth.

Cut and Glue

DRAT!

Stay back!

Paul drove into the man with gold teeth.	The man with gold teeth was stealing the cup.
The police put handcuffs on the man with gold teeth.	The crowd roared as the man tried to steal the cup.

Be Creative

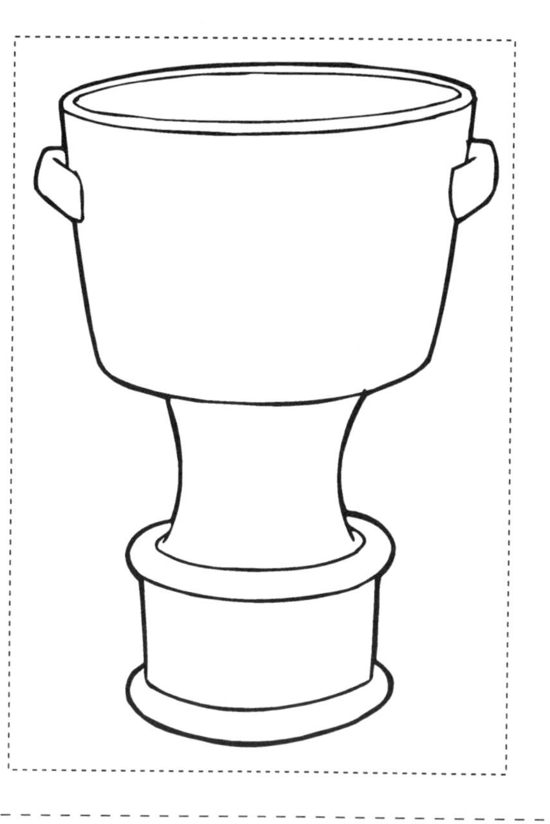

go-kart
gold cup

badge
uniform
handcuffs
radio

1. **Look at the cartoon. Find the words. Remember. Turn over. Write.**

(a) h________ (b) b________ (c) g________ c________

(d) r________ (e) u________ (f) go-________

2. **Add '*ar*' or '*or*'. Then match the words.**

(a) j________ (b) st________m

(c) f________est (d) f________m

(e) st________ (f) c________pet

bright	(e)	thunder	____
glass	____	soft	____
dark	____	sheep	____

3. **Write the missing letters. Use '*e*', '*i*' or '*u*'.**

Pa___l got ___n h___s go-kart and drov___ stra___ght at th___ man w___th gold t___ ___th. Pa___l h___t h___m w___th th___ go-kart and knock___d h___m ___nto th___ a___r.

4. **Look**

The crowd roared when they saw the man stealing the cup.

Find the words in the sentence that rhyme with:

(a) loud, proud ________________

(b) fan, pan, ran ________________

(c) then, pen, ten, ________________

(d) raw, claw, paw ________________

Paul and the Race for the Gold Cup

Chapter 14

Paul looked at the boy.

'What's your name?' he asked.

'Jack,' he replied. Then he began to tell Paul why he had helped the man with the gold teeth.

'One night, after a practice race at the stadium, the man with the gold teeth asked my father and me if we would like a lift home. We said no, but he grabbed Dad, tied him up and pushed him into his car. He told me if I ever wanted to see Dad again, I would have to win the race and hand over the gold cup. I had the fastest time until you came. The man with gold teeth thought you might win instead of me. So to stop you winning he kidnapped you.'

'So where is your Dad now?' asked Paul.

'I don't know.'

'But I do!' laughed the man with the gold teeth.

Cut and Glue

He watched you in the practice race.	He pushed Dad into the car.
He asked us if we wanted a lift.	He watched you beat my time.
He kidnapped you and threw you into the sea.	He told me to win the race.
The man with gold teeth laughed.	Paul asked Jack where his father was.

Be Creative

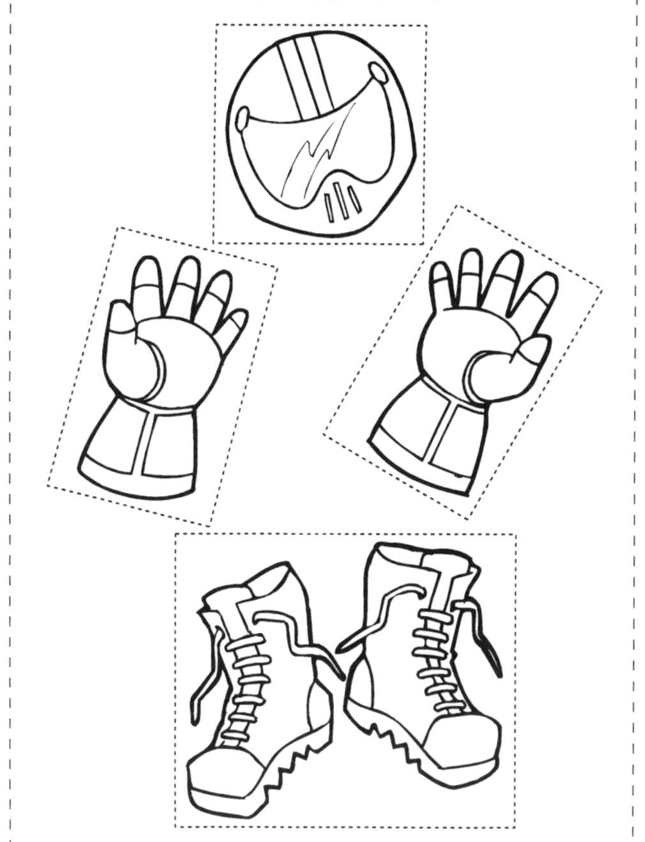

Dad
The boy told Paul
the whole story.
moon
HA
HA
coast
CLICK
CLICK
boat
grass
helmet
steering
wheel
tyres
crowd
2 MIN. 10 SEC

I don't know!
Where is your
father now?
I know where he is.
HA! HA! HA!
gold
teeth
CLICK
CLICK

1. Look at the cartoon. Find the words. Remember. Turn over. Write.

(a) s__________ w__________ (b) t__________ (c) g__________

(d) h__________ (e) c__________ (f) c__________

(g) m__________ (h) b__________ (i) D__________

2. Sort the sounds.

*tr**ou**ble*	*n**o**t*
*wh**a**t*	*d**ou**ble*
*c**o**me*	*t**o**p*
*s**o**me*	*ch**o**p*
*l**o**t*	*s**o**n*

sounds like 'f**u**n'	sounds like 'sh**o**t'
__________	__________
__________	__________
__________	__________
__________	__________
__________	__________

3. Add the missing letters. Use '**a**', '**e**', '**i**', '**o**' or '**u**'.

J__ck w__s w__rr__ __d __b__ __t h__s f__th__r.

'__ d__n't kn__w wh__r__ h__ __s,' s__ __d J__ck s__dly.

Th__ m__n w__th g__ld t__ __th l__ __gh__d wh__n h__ h__ __rd th__s.

4. Add '**t**', '**c**', '**r**', '**b**' or '**f**'.

(a) ___oast potato (b) ___oaster (c) ___oast

(d) ___oast (e) ___east (f) ___east

Paul and the Race for the Gold Cup

Chapter 15

The man's gold teeth gleamed as he spoke.

'I know I'm going to prison,' he said. 'And I know they don't allow pets there. So I'll tell you where Jack's father is—if I can keep Oswald.' Hearing his name, a white rat popped its head out of the man's pocket. Oswald was his pet rat!

'OK,' said one of the police officers. 'We'll let you keep Oswald. Now tell us where Jack's father is.' The man with the gold teeth laughed. 'Eh si ni a kcalb nav dniheb eht muidats,' he said.

Paul and Jack looked at each other. What did it mean? Then Paul had an idea. He grabbed a pencil from one of the police officers and began writing down the words.

'Look,' he said. 'He told us where your father is—but backwards!' Jack looked at the paper. Paul had written 'Eh si ni a kcalb nav dniheb eht muidats', which became 'He is in a black van behind the stadium' when written forwards.

Quick as a flash, Paul and Jack raced to the back of the stadium. There, in a black van, they found Jack's father. They were all very happy. The man with the gold teeth had been caught, and now they could all go home.

'Wait until everyone hears about my adventures,' thought Paul with a smile. Then he remembered he still had three weeks of school holidays left—and that made him smile even more.

But for the man with the gold teeth, the ending was not so happy. When Oswald—his only friend in the world—heard how long he would have to spend in jail, he ran off. Now he lives with the judge, far, far away from cold prisons. And he never thinks about his other, nasty, owner.

Cut and Glue

Paul had an idea.	The man with gold teeth said he wanted to keep Oswald.	They opened the van door.	Everyone was happy.
Paul wrote the words on a piece of paper.	Oswald, the rat, popped out of his pocket.	They saw the van.	The man with gold teeth was sent to prison for 20 years.
The boys did not understand what the man with gold teeth said.	The man with gold teeth spoke backwards.	Oswald lives beside the sea—far away from any cold prisons.	Oswald jumped into the judge's pocket.

Put in Order

I'll tell you where your father is—if I get to keep Oswald.
Eh si ni a kcalb nav dniheb eht muidats!
eh si ni a
He is in a
kcalb nav
black van
dniheb eht
behind the
muidats
stadium

Over there!

You shall go to prison for twenty years!

Take him away.

DRAT!

Answers

Chapter 1

Page 3

1. (a) clock (b) door
   (c) chair (d) pillow
   (e) window (f) bed
2. (a) socks – We wear these on our feet.
   (b) pockets – We put money in these.
   (c) rocket – We go to space in this.
   (d) clock – We tell the time with this.
3. up, nine, in, morning, it, holiday, did, up
4. (a) first (b) school
   (c) day

Chapter 2

Page 6

1. (a) stairs (b) bowl
   (c) table (d) painting
   (e) box (f) card
2. came – paint, taste, name, same
   car – hard, kart, mark
3. Paul, read, card, said, had, won, a, to, America, and, chance, to, race, Go-Kart, Gold, Paul, was
4. (a) strong (b) slow (c) stick
   (d) stairs (e) sleep (f) slip

Chapter 3

Page 9

1. (a) tree (b) seat
   (c) hotel (d) plane
   (e) road (f) wheel
2. (a) toad – This is like a big frog.
   (b) coal – This is black and we burn it.
   (c) speed – This means to travel fast.
   (d) street – Something cars drive along.
3. went, America, in, plane, There, were, more, hundred, people, in, it, The, plane, jet
4. (a) man (b) who
   (c) strange (d) saw

Chapter 4

Page 12

1. (a) gloves (b) grass
   (c) helmet (d) crowd
   (e) taxi (f) stadium
2. talk – saw, walk, tall, chalk
   taxi – can, fan, plan
3. time, minutes, ten, seconds, the, fastest, No-one, else, beat, sure, he, win, real, race
4. (a) cream (b) trumpet
   (c) stream (d) crowd
   (e) stripes (f) string

Chapter 5

Page 15

1. (a) hood (b) hamburger
   (c) rope (d) glass
   (e) lamp (f) hand
2. (a) glass – It is easy to break.
   (b) swing – It is something we play on.
   (c) switch – It is either off or on.
   (d) sweep – It is what we do when we use a broom.
3. Suddenly, Paul, a, hand, jumped, up, but, up, and, head, out
4. (a) bed (b) fast
   (c) got (d) he

Chapter 6

Page18

1. (a) moon (b) starfish
   (c) boat (d) truck
   (e) jetty (f) headlights
2. boat – snow, below, crow, goat
   moon – tube, roof, rude, spoon
3. After, a, while, the, stopped, Paul, could, not, see, anything, he, noticed, that, the, air, smelt, salty, and, there, was, the, noise, of, waves, the, distance
4. (a) fight – This is what boxers do.
   (b) light – This is bright.
   (c) night – This is when we can see stars.
   (d) height – This is how tall you are.

Chapter 7

Page 21

1. (a) chain (b) anchor
   (c) deck (d) porthole
   (e) bow (f) cabin
2. (a) trick – Not real. It's magic.
   (b) neck – Not your shoulders.
   (c) quick – Not slow.
   (d) shipwreck – Not a ship to sail in.
3. Suddenly, Paul, was, up, and, thrown, into, sea, landed, water, a, huge, splash, kidnappers, just, laughed
4. (a) Paul (b) boat (c) thud
   (d) deck

Chapter 8

Page 24

1. (a) surprised (b) fin
   (c) mast (d) coast
   (e) angry (f) sad
2. find – tie, shine, light, fight
   fin – ginger, winner, swimmer, him
3. boat, sailed, away, Paul, afraid, coast, was, too, far, to, swim, to, Paul, was, alone, in, middle, of, sea, with, no-one, to, him
4. (a) barking (b) turn
   (c) marker pen (d) shark
   (e) furniture (f) burn

Chapter 9

Page 27

1. (a) happy (b) mouth
   (c) eye (d) teeth
   (e) nose (f) dolphin
2. (a) case (b) hose
   (c) base (d) nose
   (e) rose (f) paste
   long (b), heavy (a), sticky (f), red (e), runny (d), secret (c)
3. Paul, huge, gleaming, in, moonlight, afraid, sure, about, to, him, for, dinner
4. (a) dry (b) three
   (c) pull (d) land

Answers

Chapter 10

Page 30

1. (a) car park (b) suit
   (c) gold teeth (d) white hat
   (e) four (f) nine
2. teeth – peanut, please, sleep, speak, we
   ten – next, left, tent, plenty, ready
3. Paul, ran, inside, the, stadium, and, went, straight, his, go-kart, Luckily, the, race, had, started, yet, He, was, about, his, helmet, when, he, heard, a, strange, noise
4. (a) folder (b) lolly
   (c) soldier (d) cold
   (e) rollercoaster (f) doll

Chapter 11

Page 33

1. (a) red (b) steering wheel
   (c) green (d) bell
   (e) twelve (f) tyres
2. (a) shirt (b) thirty
   (c) fire (d) firework
   (e) wire (f) birthday

   happy (f), warm (c), sharp (e), clean (a), number (b), loud (d)
3. Paul, line, when, he, remembered, there, been, two, people, hotel, room, the, boat
4. (a) race (b) lights
   (c) red (d) green

Chapter 12

Page 36

1. (a) crash (b) pull
   (c) shout (d) explode
   (e) watch (f) race
2. shout – shower, power, mouse, tower, hour
   shut – must, jump, come, brush, upstairs
3. After, boy, number, crashed, crowd, Paul, to, stop, Paul, had, not, stopped, would, have, won, Because, Paul, stop, boy, was, not, badly, hurt
4. (a) goldfish (b) smash
   (c) wish (d) rash
   (e) crash (f) dish

Chapter 13

Page 39

1. (a) handcuffs (b) badge
   (c) gold cup (d) radio
   (e) uniform (f) go-kart
2. (a) jar (b) storm
   (c) forest (d) farm
   (e) star (f) carpet

   bright (e), thunder (b), glass (a), soft (f), dark (c), sheep (d)
3. Paul, in, his, drove, straight, the, with, teeth, Paul, hit, him, with, the, knocked, him, into, the, air
4. (a) crowd (b) man (c) when (d) saw

Chapter 14

Page 42

1. (a) steering wheel
   (b) tyres (c) grass
   (d) helmet (e) crowd
   (f) coast (g) moon
   (h) boat (i) Dad
2. fun – trouble, double, come, some, son
   shot – not, what, top, chop, lot
3. Jack was worried about his father. 'I don't know where he is,' said Jack sadly.
   The man with gold teeth laughed when he heard this.
4. (a) roast potato (b) toaster
   (c) toast (d) coast
   (e) beast (f) feast